The POET

STRIKES AGAIN

Andy Tooze

ILLUSTRATED by Martin Olsson

Matador
9 Priory Business Park,
Wistow Road, Kibworth Beauchamp,
Leicestershire. LE8 0RX
Tel: 0116 279 2299
Email: books@troubador.co.uk
Web: www.troubador.co.uk/matador
Twitter: @matadorbooks

ISBN 978 1789013 375

British Library Cataloguing in Publication Data.
A catalogue record for this book is available from the British Library.

Printed and bound by CPI Group (UK) Ltd, Croydon, CR0 4YY
Typeset in 14pt Aldine401 BT by Troubador Publishing Ltd, Leicester, UK

Matador is an imprint of Troubador Publishing Ltd

Dedicated to Tyla, Alyssa and Amelia
with love.

Andy Tooze

www.thepoetfromthepeaks.co.uk

contents

Me And My Mind

Be Yourself

Bodies

The Not so old

Animals (especially cats)

Fragile Nature

Twenty Words

Riddles and Endings

Openings

Number One

It stands so proud and tall,
The greatest number of them all.
Numero Uno, bettered by none,
The first, the only, number one.

The original number, the stand alone,
In a class all of its own.
It's mathematics one true hero,
One step up from the emptiness of zero.

The pop stars want to reach it,
Footballers aim for it too.
Everyone wants to be number one,
It's so much better than number two.

One is the special number,
It rules over all the rest.
It's a number made in heaven,
The chosen one, the best.

Happiness

Lazy morning,
Gently yawning.
Monday at nine,
No rush this time.
I'll stay in bed until late,
Everything can wait.
The grey clouds break to reveal the sun,
My school holiday has just begun.

Bricks

Bricks are rectangular,
Heavy and angular.
Not much use when all alone,
But put lots together
And you've got a home.

CLIMBING

You climb and clamber,
Rock by rock,
On and on,
To the top.

At the summit
Shout 'Yahoo!'
Then it's down again
For you!

 4

Fashion

There are leggings and treggings and jeggings,
Footless tights, footfull tights and dresses.
Skirts, wraps,
Trousers short and long.
If you fancy being flamboyant
You could even wear a sarong.
Girls tend to have options.
For boys though, maybe not.
It's long trousers when it's cold.
Maybe short ones when it's hot.
For girls variety is the name of the game.
For boys it's usually more of the same.

Manchester

Football divider,
Hope provider,
Bee buzzer,
Division fuzzer.
Cloud drencher,
Desire quencher,
Town crier,
Angels choir.
Ariana Grand,
United stand,
Heavens above,
One Love.

 6

Months

January jumps,
February frolics,
March marches,
April appears,
May moves,
June jives,
July jiggles,
August advances,
September strides,
October opens,
November notes,
December decides …
It's Christmas!

7

Poetry

Poems can be very short or incredibly long.
They can be set to music
To make a jolly song.
They can rhyme or not,
It all depends you see.
A poem can do almost anything,
Except make a cup of tea.

School

No idea

No idea, no idea,
I've absolutely no idea.
It could be twelve or maybe three,
Basically just don't ask me.
If I had the slightest clue,
You can be sure I would tell you.
Dearest teacher I've made it clear,
I've absolutely no idea.

Autumn Playtime

In the playground
Someone falls,
Everyone gathers around.

In the playground
Someone calls,
A stray jumper has been found.

In the playground
Two heads bump,
Making children cry.

In the playground
Someone jumps,
High towards the sky.

In the playground
Leaves fall,
Coats fight Autumn's chill.

In the playground
The bell rings,
Everyone stands still.

The Disco Bus

Come with us, come with us,
Jump aboard the disco bus.
Our bus driver really rocks,
From his groovy hat to his crazy socks.

He will play your favourite song,
Then everyone will sing along.
Before you are halfway there,
You'll have joy in your heart,
And glitter in your hair.

In our school
You know you're winning,
When it's your turn
To go swimming.

You'll never hear a word of fuss
When we climb onto the bus.
Come with us, come with us,
Jump aboard the disco bus!

The Balloon Teacher

He started every lesson the very same way,
"Children don't let me down," he would say.
I'm pleased to tell that all went well,
Until one morning,
Quite without warning,
Stephen Stevens got a pin,
Crept up to him,
And stuck it in.

The balloon teacher made a hissing noise,
Which silenced the chattering girls and boys.
He then flew crazily around the room
Shouting, "You've let me down. It is my doom,
Stephen Stevens, you're for it now."
But his threats were useless anyhow,
Because all of the chatter finally stopped,
When the balloon teacher simply popped!

Sports Day

Arms a pumping,
Legs a thumping,
Crowd a cheering,
Tape a nearing,
Lips a grinning,
Race a winning!

New School

New hopes, new fears,
Down to breakfast holding back tears.
New bag, new lunchbox,
Clean shirt, pulled up socks.

Take a deep breath.
It's time to set off.
Out into the street,
With a nervous cough.

A million new challenges,
Both at work and at play.
My life starts again,
At my new school today.

The First Lunchtime

I want to see my mummy,
I want to see her now.
I've got a painful tummy,
I'm really missing her, ow!

I want to see my mummy,
She told me school was great.
But she didn't see the cabbage
They loaded on my plate.

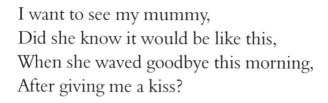

I want to see my mummy,
I really want to cry.
I didn't eat the cabbage
And I left my apple pie.

I want to see my mummy,
Did she know it would be like this,
When she waved goodbye this morning,
After giving me a kiss?

I want to see my mummy,
To tell her she wasn't right,
When she said I'd make new friends
And learn to read and write.

I want to see my mummy,
Some boys want me to play.
I might as well join in,
As I know I've got to stay.

I want to see my mummy,
After this football match.
I'm a brilliant goalie,
I've just made an amazing catch.

I want to see my mummy,
To tell her my team won.
She knows a lot my mummy,
She told me school was fun.

I want to see my mummy,
But not until after three.
That's quite soon enough
For a great big boy like me!

The Lollipop Lady

The lollipop lady can be clearly seen
At the side of the road wearing yellow and green.
She leans on her stick as she stares around,
She seems to sense something.
What has she found?

Her nose starts to twitch.
Is that petrol in the air?
Her whole body tenses,
From her toes to her hair.

Now she is certain,
There's a car on the way.
The very first challenge
Of her working day.

Not a moment to lose,
She must act now.
To her it's alive,
A mechanical cow.

It must be stopped.
She picks up her stick,
Then charges straight at it.
She's nimble and quick.

Mrs Lolly is charging as fast as a train.
The driver blinks, gulps, then blinks again.
He panics, confused,
Has the world gone insane?
The car turns around,
Racing off the way that it came.

The children are cheering.
Mrs Lolly has won.
The early morning score is:
Cars nil, the lollipop lady one!

The Giggles

"You are charged with giggling, how do you plead?"
"Please Miss, I'm guilty,"
"You are guilty indeed,
You're far too silly, School should not be fun."

The speech goes on and on and on.
But I'm not listening any more,
I've spotted something hairy,
Scuttling across the floor.

Where's the spider crawling to?
It's climbing on the teacher's shoe.
While she drones on and on about me,
The spider keeps climbing, it's up to her knee.

She sees it, she shrieks, she starts to dance.
Her spell is broken, I'm out of my trance.
I'm on the floor giggling like mad,
The worst fit of giggles I've ever had.

I must look like a spider myself,
With my legs flailing in the air,
As the teacher searches frantically
For the spider in her hair.

In time, I'm sure I'll recover,
And life will be normal again.
But for now I've got the giggles,
The world's sweetest pain!

Oddities

Martians

If you ever meet a Martian
Don't forget to say,
"Hippy, glippy, gloppy,"
As he passes on his way.

If he really is a Martian,
He will thoughtfully reply,
"Hurgle, turgle, gurgle,"
Which means hello, goodbye.

The Man Without A Skeleton

The man without a skeleton couldn't stay upright.
However hard he tried he couldn't get it right.
The man without a skeleton had other problems besides.
Without the bones to keep them in
He had troublesome insides.

Sometimes they would escape and spill out onto the floor.
Once I saw his lungs and kidneys heading for the door.
His heart would sit in a corner
Pounding sadly on its own.
It is a terrible thing to be born without a bone.

Each night he would complain,
"I'm at the end of my tether,
Oh how I wish that I could just pull myself together!"

The centipede Twins Start School

Jake the bright, young centipede
Had all the gear that he would need.
A shiny uniform and a hundred shoes,
The colours of which he was allowed to choose.

Jake chose ten of every colour,
Except for pink.
He said, "Pink is for girls. That's what I think."

But Jake's twin sister Emily
Did not agree,
"I do not think pink shoes look right on me."

I wonder what's left in the centipede shoe shop?
I'll tell you what I think:
Lots of lovely, tiny shoes,
Mostly coloured pink.

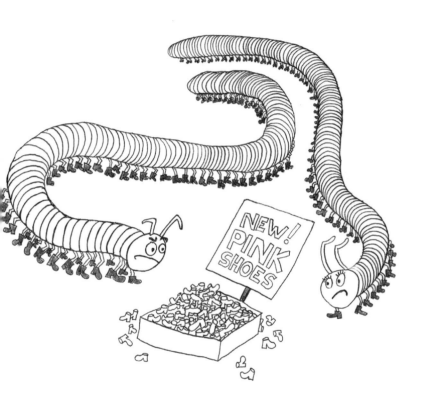

Alphabetical Brains

Alphabetical brains can do everything.
Forget guessing.
Happy immediately.
Joyfully know lots more new, original people.
Quick, really smart teachers understand.
Very wicked.
Xceptional.
Yeah.
Zeydidn'tknowalphabeticalbrainswerezo
amazingdidzey!

Home Grown Alien

Tongues are strange, alien creatures.
Think about your tongue.
Now move it around.
Touch your teeth.
Curl it up, if you can.
Touch the roof of your mouth.
Stick it out.

What's it like?
Nothing.
Why is it always wet?
Who knows?
What's it made of?
Strange stuff.

Have you ever bitten your tongue?
It's agony for a moment,
But in a flash it's completely better.
It's magical.
Why?
It's a mystery.

Your tongue is an alien.
Do you trust it?

The Animals United v England Football Match

The roughest football team ever seen
Was the Animals United Mean Machine.
The bull was a bully.
The crocodile crocked.
Everyone in the crowd was astonished and
shocked.

The python tied the goalkeeper into a knot
To leave the elephant an easy shot.
If an England player went down,
Down he stayed.
Even the ref was becoming afraid.

For when he brandished the card coloured yellow
The hyenas laughed and cried,
"What a foolish fellow.
If he decides to turn yellow to red,
We'll stop laughing and eat him instead."

England lost the game,
It hardly needs saying,
But just remember who they were playing:
The roughest football team ever seen.
The Animals United Mean Machine!

Pub Grub

My local pub serves lovely grub:
Jacket potatoes, sausages, sandwiches too,
Toasties and boasties and sugar on glue.
Fried cat's whiskers and piggy wig rings,
All served with a salad of dinosaur wings!

An Odd Body Poem

A nose is just too nosy.
An ear is just too eerie.
An arm can join the army.
This poem is just barmy.

The Staring contest

The boy and the girl had a staring contest,
It was like they were frozen in time.
A weird, freeze frame moment,
Now immortalized in rhyme.
I didn't understand the rules,
Why it started, why it carried on?
But suddenly by some unspoken agreement,
They unlocked eyes
And the moment was gone.

Mars

Red planet,
Spaceships scan it,
Children eat it,
You can't beat it.
Planet or bars:
Mars.

Me And My Mind

The Fish Tank

My brain is like a fish tank,
Constantly bubbly,
Unignorably troubly.
I think my brain may contain fish.

Stretching

Stretching out for victory,
Stretching out for hope.
Stretching out into the world,
Hope that I can cope.

Sometimes I want to curl
Into a human ball.
To block out all the nonsense,
I just can't stretch at all.

But then the energy returns,
I regain my inner shout.
So I start to stretch again,
Out, out, out!

37

May

May there always be birds singing like this.
May there always be someone to give me a kiss.
May there always be someone to be by my side.
May there never be a time when I just have to hide
Who I am and how I feel.
May I always know that love is real!

 38

Origins

Which came first,
The chicken or the egg?
Which grew first,
The arm or the leg?
Who loved first,
The woman or the man?
Who knew first?
God says: "I Am."

Mum's Bone

My mum kept a human thigh bone,
A femur, in our home.
She would bring the femur into the front room,
To show it to visitors, like a family heirloom.
The femur is the longest human bone,
But people don't usually keep them at home.
Mum's bone was long, thin and white,
It really was a distinctive sight.
She only borrowed it at first, so she said,
But she ended up keeping it forever.
It became our family's special treasure.

It seemed normal to me, you see,
Keeping that bone in our home.
Looking back, it wasn't so normal really,
But my mum loved her bone,
We could see that clearly.
Next time you look at someone's thigh,
In your mind's eye,
Please see my mum,
And remember her bone,
In our home!

41

At The End Is You

When all seems at an end,
And not one friend seems true,
When I don't know where to turn,
At the end is you.

When I've mucked up again,
And got things badly wrong,
When I never seem to learn,
It's then I hear your song.

When I'm not sure who I am,
Or where I might be going,
When I'm curled up in despair,
For there seems no way of knowing.

It's then that you grasp me,
And hold me so tight,
You whisper fresh hope,
Tell me things will be all right.

When all seems at an end,
And I don't know what to do,
When I don't know where to turn,
At the end is you.

Two

Two are a pair.
Two can share.
Play together,
Laugh together,
Cry together.
Together.
Get it?
Two.
Me and you!

 44

A Rap About Me

My future is out of my hands,
My future is in my feet.
I'm the dancing, footballing poet
Who always feels the beat.

I dance past the defenders
And the attackers too.
And if you try to tackle me
I'll dance past you.

I will think up a rhyme
As quick as a flash,
Mix the words together
Into a magical mash.

I'm the dancing, footballing poet,
With magic in my shoes.
Poems race around my head,
My name is Andy Tooze.

The Born Identity

I am me, me, only me,
With my own identity.
My own blood, my own skin
Which I feel so happy in.

But what if I was a boy
Who wanted to be a girl?
Or a girl
Who wanted to be a boy?
So that who I was
Was not someone I could enjoy.

Would I fight to be able to
Change my body to fit my mind,
So that I could leave
My born identity behind?

Be Yourself

Think Again

You think you know me,
But you don't.
You think I'm stupid,
But I'm not.
You think I don't care,
But I do.
You think you're better than me,
But that's not true.
I'm just different from you!

Get Up and Go

If your get up and go
Has got up and gone,
Go out and get it back.
Without your get up and go
You'll be sad and slow,
So don't wait for a moment.
Attack!

Wherever your get up and go has gone,
You really must get it back.
Without your get up and go,
Every yes will be no,
And your body and mind will go slack.

The first place to search is the sea of sadness,
So dive deep and see if it's there.
Another is the mountain of exhaustion,
But only climb up it with care.
Wherever you find your get up and go,
Make sure you hold it tight.
It may try to escape again,
Without it you'll never be right.

If your get up and go
Has got up and gone,
Go out and get it back.
Without your get up and go
You'll be sad and slow,
So don't wait for a moment.
Attack!

Split Down The Middle

Here is my riddle:
I'm split down the middle,
I've decided I'm divided in two.
The cause of this decision,
This heart aching incision,
Is not knowing what I should do.

What's come about,
Is that Dad's moved out.
So Mum told me "It's up to you.
You can move in with your Dad."
But I know she'd be sad.
So I just don't know what to do.

I know it's up to me,
But it's tricky you see,
For I just don't have a clue.
My family is splitting,
My insides are ripping.
Oh what on earth should I do?

Outside The Box

Think outside the box.
Go on have a go.
The next time they tell you how to think,
You just tell them 'No!'

Think outside the box.
Don't let others rule your mind.
Develop your own style and smile,
Because you are one of a kind!

i'm Shy

I'm shy,
I don't know why.
I try not to be so shy,
But when the teacher catches my eye,
And asks me questions in front of everyone,
My legs turn to jelly,
My face turns red,
And I wish that I was somewhere else instead.

The Deep

Push out into the deep.
It's the only way,
Unless you want to stay
Safe and secure
By the shore,
While everyone else is bobbing around:
Laughing, joking, growing, exploring,
Succeeding,
Exceeding what they thought they could do.
It could be the same for you.
Go on,
Be brave.
There's more,
Explore.
Push out, push out,
Push out into the deep!

Dreamdust

Never forget that your dreams are magic dust.
They may be ancient and grimy,
But keep them you must.
For if you don't hold them tight,
Both at work and at play,
Your dreamdust will scatter,
Far, far away.

Days

Walking days are okay.
Running days are great.
Racing, chasing, leaping,
The world is your best mate.

Some days though are crawling days,
Everything seems tough.
Crawling is quite painful,
Your knees just scream: Enough!

Then you get the flying days,
The world slips far below.
Everything looks glorious,
The lights are green for go.

The Peacock

Shake those tail feathers,
Shake them out,
So the whole, wide world
Can see what you're about.

If they don't like your colours,
If they tell you you're vain,
Shake them anyway,
They are a fiery flame.
They show who you are,
That you love as you choose,
You decide for yourself,
You make your own news.

For you are the peacock,
Bold and bright,
To shake your tail feathers,
Is your delight!

Bodies

Skin

Skin is both very tough,
And very thin.
It keeps outside things out,
And inside things in.

Sniffle Snuffle

Sniffle snuffle,
Sniffle snuffle,
I'm really feeling ill.

Sniffle snuffle,
Sniffle snuffle,
I think I've caught a chill.

Sniffle snuffle,
Sniffle snuffle,
There's throbbing in my head.

Sniffle snuffle,
Sniffle snuffle,
Please can I go to bed?

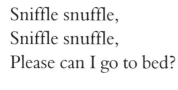

The Body

The brain is a thinker.
The eye is a winker.
The heart is for lovers.
The fingers are brothers.
The teeth are biters.
The knuckles are fighters.
The nose is a sniffer.
The bottom's a whiffer!

Eyelashes

They're gentle protectors,
Damage detectors.
They flutter and flick,
They're ever so quick.
They're soft as a whisper,
Thin as a flea.
They take care of themselves,
And they look after me.

Nails

A fingernail is not a quick grower,
But a toenail is even slower.

Lungs

In out, in out,
First breath, baby's cry.
Mum gives contented sigh.

In out, in out,
Final breath before you die.
One tear from your eye.

In out, in out,
Loved ones say goodbye.

First breath, last breath,
From birth to death.

In out, in out …out!

Tongues

They're moovy, groovy,
Sticky, licky,
Covered in saliva.
Tongues aren't good at staying still,
Or keeping dry either.

Naughty Nose

Naughty nose, naughty nose,
Sniffing out trouble.

Naughty nose, naughty nose,
Making it double.

Naughty nose, naughty nose,
Leading me where I nose I shouldn't be.

My mum says it's not my nose that's naughty.
My mum says it's me!

My Brain

Do I control my brain,
Or does it control me?
My brain and me,
Such strange company.

The Not So Old

A Baby Dragon

A baby dragon is fast asleep with a
Snore, snore, snore.
A baby dragon is waking up with a
Roar, roar, roar.
A baby dragon says, "Good morning Mum."
Kiss, kiss, kiss.
A baby dragon has a wake up wash,
Splash, splosh, splish.
A baby dragon breathes fire on bread to make
Toast, toast, toast.
Buttery toast is the breakfast it likes the
Most, most, most.

A Baby Dinosaur

A baby dinosaur is eating a banana.
Munch, munch, munch.
A baby dinosaur is gobbling a sandwich.
Lunch, lunch, lunch.
A baby dinosaur is having a bath.
Splash, splash, splash.
A baby dinosaur is so clumsy.
Crash, crash, crash.
A baby dinosaur is turning somersaults.
Roll, roll, roll.
A baby dinosaur is playing football.
GOAL, GOAL, GOAL!

Trees

Why are trees so big and tall,
When I am really rather small?
Were they small once just like me,
And do their leaves help them to see?

Baby

Lots of tears,
Not much hair.
Baggy nappy always there.
Making sounds like
Gurgle goo.
Not so long ago,
That was you!

Wink

Wink with one eye,
Blink with two,
Nod your head,
How do you do?

Raise your eyebrows,
Touch your nose,
Wave both hands,
That's how it goes.

Now you've played this funny game,
Let's speed it up,
And do it again.

Wink with one eye,
Blink with two,
Nod your head,
How do you do?

Raise your eyebrows,
Touch your nose,
Wave both hands,
That's how it goes.

Groovy Moves

Twitch your nose,
Wriggle your toes,
One, two, three.

Rub your tum,
Put up a thumb,
Listen carefully.

Sway your hips,
Lick your lips,
This is what you do.

Point to an ear,
Shake your rear,
Cock -a -doodle-do!

Bathtime

The Moon goes round the Earth,
And the Earth goes round the Sun,
While I send my mum into orbit,
When I'm only having fun,
By splashing wildly in the bath,
Until the bath is on the floor.
Then I shout loudly to my mum,
"Can I have some more?"

Miles Of Smiles

Miles of smiles,
Oodles of fun,
Chasing my brother,
Hugging my mum.

Miles of smiles,
Warm, soggy toast,
Frost on the hillside,
A card through the post.

Miles of smiles,
A swim in the sea,
A crab on the beach
Is dancing with me.

Miles of smiles,
Whispers in the dark,
Snow covered gardens,
Games in the park.

Miles of smiles,
Killing my fears,
Giggles and laughter,
Drowning my tears.

The Talking Plate

The talking plate just loves to play,
So lunchtime's her favourite time of day.
When the dinner ladies put her out at noon,
She chats to her knife, her fork and her spoon.
When after lunch they wash her up,
She swims in the soapsuds,
And laughs with her cup.
As she's dried she squeals with delight,
Before she's stacked away out of sight.

It's a simple life for a talking plate.
I'd find it boring,
But she thinks it's great.

Tiny Tot

Tiny tot tottering,
Toddling along,
Singing to herself
This tiny tot song.

"I'm a dinky, little tiny tot,
I've just learned how to talk.
I'm doing lots of learning,
I'm learning how to walk.

But walking is so tricky,
I keep falling on the floor,
Because I've only got two legs
While cats and dogs have four."

Animals
(especially cats)

Bouncing

Bouncing on the carpet,
Springing in the air,
Playfully cavorting,
Jumping everywhere.

I love to sit and watch them,
Leaping from the ground,
Our lively, little cat fleas,
Bouncing all around.

catellite TV

On Catellite TV cats are everywhere.
If you don't like cats you'd better beware,
Because 'The Cat Factor' and 'Strictly Come Purring'
Are on every Saturday night.
Sometimes there's even a late night catfight.

You might prefer to watch cats at play
On that cattastic football show, 'Cat of the Day',
Where teams of cats chase a ball of string,
Leaping and bouncing, giving it everything.

If you want to watch Catellite TV
Just get yourself a dish,
Then fill it with milk and bits of fish.

The Pet

Her padding paws
Have razor claws,
Licked clean.

Dark night stalker,
High wall walker,
Sleek, mean.

In midnight fights,
She scratches, bites,
Seldom seen.

Although all know
Her chilling call.
Caterwaul!

A cat's Life

Is there still room in the circle of doom
For one more struggling cat?
I've been chasing the birds for a year and a day,
With my plan to knock them out flat.

But they fly away with their fluttering wings.
Birds really are frustrating things.

So I've made a decision, a change of plan.
I'm finished with birds, for I've caught a man.

Now he feeds me every day out of a tin.
The wild life out. The easy life in.

81

chameLeons

Chameleons are lizards,
Wizards, deceivers,
Believers that they'll be harder to spot,
If they change colour a lot.

Chameleons are
Colour shifters,
Rocky drifters.

In the world of Humans
They are famous.
Lizard celebrities!

Sloppy

Sloppy the slow, slimy slug
Is no ordinary bug.
He carries his home on his back,
Like a postman with his sack.
But Sloppy does not deliver the mail,
Because Sloppy the slug is really a snail!

Fragile Nature

One World

One world, one hope,
One fragile ecosystem
Struggling to cope.
One crowded, vibrant planet
In all of outer space.
One crazy bunch of polluters:
The human race!

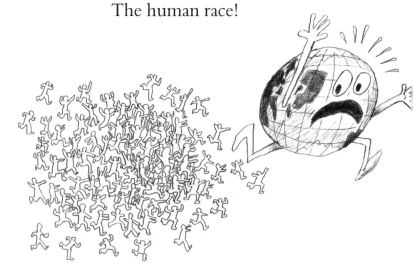

Meltdown

The Earth's heating up,
Bit by bit.
The Arctic ice is melting,
Drip by drip.
The jungle's disappearing,
Tree by tree.
Our planet's sick,
Can't you see?

Night Storm

Listen to the crashing waves
Battering the shore,
As the runaway horses
Race around once more.

Galloping crazily,
They're fierce and free.
It's a race they've been running
For eternity.

See the froth foaming,
Taste their salty breath,
As they challenge the world,
"Come dice with death."

Many a life the waves have stolen,
On a night such as this,
When they possess the power
Of a Dementor's kiss.

They are irresistibly strong,
These wild horses of the sea.
In a million years from now,
They will still be running free.

The Seabed

The seabed isn't a bed
On which to rest your head.
It's a wetland of
Seaweed swaying,
Seahorse playing
Wonder.

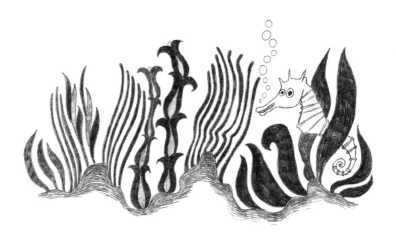

The Last Leaf of Autumn

The last leaf of Autumn
Has just fluttered down.
The final ruby has fallen
From the royal crown.
The late departing guest
Has left before the snow,
As the leaf's inner voice called,
"Join the others, go."
The last leaf of Autumn
Has just fluttered down.
The trees are bare,
Quite leafless now.
Winter's come to town.

Colours

Out of the blue,
Into the red,
Colours dance around my head.
Green, orange, yellow, pink,
A rainbow of brightness,
To make me think
That a world without colour
Would be a dull, drab sight,
Like old style movies,
Black and white.

Autumn

Shiny conkers
As bright as a berry.
Fiery fireworks
As red as a cherry.
Ghostly mists
As grey as death.
First frosts,
Watch your breath!

91

Summer

Gentle, lilting breeze,
Trees are dressed in green.
Winter is over,
Warmth has won.
Finally, happily,
Summer has come.

 92

Twenty Words

Twenty Words About Dictionaries

Books of words,
About meanings of words.
Sometimes they're simple,
Sometimes not.
Meanings of words
Is what dictionaries have got.

Twenty Words About Love

Only love can save us.
Only love will make us
Brave enough
To overcome hate.
Don't wait!
Choose love now.

Twenty Words About Geese

My heroes and heroines
Of the natural world.
Triathlon champions,
Swimming, flying and waddling.
Their flying formation?
V for victory!

Twenty Words About Sweets

Suck them, chuck them,
Chew them, boo them,
Try them, buy them,
Crunch them, munch them.
Then clean your teeth!

Twenty Words About Growing

I'm changing.
Not the old me,
Not the me still to be.
The new me,
The now me,
The Changeling.

ME AS BABY

Twenty Words About Potatoes

Potatoes are Britain's legendary vegetables.
Carrot, smarrot,
Broccoli, sproccoli,
Brussell sprout, out,
Cauliflower, what a shower,
But potatoes?
Absolute legends!

Twenty Words About An Eyebrow

An eyebrow is highbrow entertainment.
It's full of fun.
An eyebrow is a curvy, wurvy wonder,
The hairy little monster!

Twenty Words
About Karate Rabbits

Black belts, blue bandanas,
Ears pinned back, twitchy whiskers.
Karate rabbits strive
For the ultimate prize.
A pile of carrots!

Riddles and Endings

The Shopping Race

Shop, shop until you drop,
Buy it all, buy it now.
Buy it quickly,
Bought it.
Wow!

Next shop, lickety lick,
Got to be quick,
Got to be slick.
Shop, shop until you drop,
I think that I am going to pop.

Race, race, fast, fast,
Leave the others in the past.
Rush around, no chance of snoring,
Although in my opinion,
Shopping's boring!

Who's The Salesman?

Roll up, roll up,
Free go, free go.
I have a trampoline,
It's the best in the world you know.

It's bouncy.
It's springy.
It's wonderfully zingy.

Yes Sir,
That's right,
A free go, I said.
Where did you hear about my trampoline?
Oh yes,
On the web.

You Madam,
You were just passing by?
It's your lucky day,
On my trampoline you can fly.

No sir,
Your children won't get stuck,
I've planned it carefully,
I don't rely on luck.

I've made the trampoline all by myself.
It's not just plucked from a dusty shelf.

Now if you're all ready,
It's time to jump.

One, two, three, Wheeee!

Answer on page 113

103

The Prisoner

I'm the prisoner,
Looking for an escape route.
Darting endlessly,
Here and there,
But I never make it to freedom.
So I make the best of it
By keeping my prison cell clean and tidy,
Although it's a full time job
With all the rubbish that gets thrown in here.
Then there's the talking,
I get no choice.
I have to do it.
I'm only given a glimpse of freedom
When my boss is being rude.

Do you know who I am?

Here's a clue.
I'm part of you.

Answer on page 113

You

Ancient and modern,
Old and new.
The past and the present
Combine in you.

All of your ancestors
Made you who you are.
In order to be you
You've travelled so far.

But here you are
Reading this poem.
As for the future?
There's no way of knowing.

Wheels

My Peugeot 107,
My little slice of heaven.

Keeps me safe and sound, mile after mile.
Some say it's not the ultimate in style.

But I think it is.
Whizz, whizz, whizz!

The Future

The future's coming,
It's on its way.
We know that tomorrow
Will follow today.

The future's coming,
We can't avoid it.
We can't outrace it,
Better to embrace it.

The future's coming,
The future's near.
Yet strangely enough
It's never here.

Today's The Day

Today's the day.
It's the only day we've got.
Yesterday's gone, tomorrow never comes,
But today we're burning hot.

Today we're breaking out
Of cages that contain us.
Today we're searching
For soul food to sustain us.

Today we are going to be
The people who we want to be.

Today we're forgetting failures from our past.
Today we're forgetting that today can never last.

Today we believe
In what we can achieve
In just one day.

Today!

 108

YESTERDAY TODAY TOMORROW

109

The World Of Books

Falling down the rabbit hole
Is just what Alice did.
Adventures are everywhere
When you are a kid.

But as you get older,
And pressures start to grow,
Where can you find a haven,
A safe place to go?

The world of books
Is a world of hope.
It can help you to thrive
Not just to cope.

It can whisk you away
To a place of joy,
Where every new story
Is like a new Christmas toy.

 110

Alice ended up
In Wonderland.
If you love books,
You'll understand.

The Refugee

They say there are too many of us,
But there is no us,
Just people like me,
A solitary refugee,
Yearning for his family.
I feel like I've been cut in two,
Sawn and sawn and sawn right through.
I just don't know what else to do,
Apart from calling
HELP!

Riddle Answers

Who's The Salesman?
  A Spider!

The Prisoner
  A Tongue!

Martin Olsson

www.olssonmartin.wixsite.com/professorillustrator

Also by Andy Tooze

The Poetry Bug

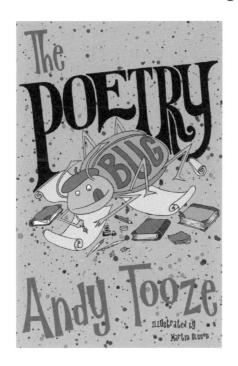

Published by Matador 2016